THE RANDOM HOUSE ACHIEVEMENT PROGRAM IN
LITERATURE

READING AND LITERATURE CONSULTANTS

TOM WOLPERT • LEE BENNETT HOPKINS

REVIEWERS

MEI-LING SHIROISHI • **JACKIE MATTHEWS**

Library-Media Specialist   *Curriculum Supervisor*
Chehalem Elementary School   *Hillsborough County Schools*
Beaverton, Oregon   *Tampa, Florida*

Project Editor: Michael A. Ross
Senior Manufacturing Associate: Catherine Bokman
Design and Production: Dimensions and Directions, Ltd.
Composition: Grafacon, Inc.
Cover Photo: Lee L. Walman, The Stock Market, Inc.
Photo Research: Helena Frost

ART AND PHOTO CREDIT LIST:

2, Morissa Lipstein; **3,** Diane Paterson; **9,** Grant Heilman, Inc.; **10,** Susan Swan; **12–18,** Diane Paterson; **19–24,** Olivia Cole Hauptfleisch; **25,** William E. Frost, Frost Publishing Group, Ltd.; **26, 27,** Anne Kennedy; **28–33,** Michele A. Noiset; **34,** Olivia Cole Hauptfleisch; **48–49,** Grant Heilman, Inc.; **50–51,** B. Todd; **52–53,** George Ulrich; **76–79,** Susan Swan; **127,** Runk, Grant Heilman, Inc.; **128,** Grant Heilman, Inc.; **129,** Tom McHugh, Photo Researchers, Inc.; **130,** Jay M. Steinberg, Photo Researchers, Inc.; **131, 132,** Grant Heilman, Inc.; **133,** Michael Heron; **134–144,** Morissa Lipstein.

Manufactured in the United States of America   ISBN 676-39724-7   789HL543

ACKNOWLEDGMENTS

Grateful acknowledgment is made to the following authors, agents and publishers for permission to use copyrighted materials:

Annick Press Ltd. for "Mud Puddle" © 1979 Robert Munsch, MUD PUDDLE, Annick Press Ltd. Toronto, Canada.

Atheneum Publishers, Inc.: Lilian Moore, "In the Fog" from the collection SOMETHING NEW BEGINS. Copyright © 1982 Lilian Moore. Reprinted with the permission of Atheneum Publishers, Inc.

Carolrhoda Books, Inc. for "Mary Ann the Witch Girl" from THE CAT WALKED THROUGH THE CASSEROLE, copyright © 1984 by Pamela Espeland and Marilyn Waniek. Published by Carolrhoda Books, Inc. Used by permission of the publisher.

Curtis Brown, Ltd. for "Nighttime" by Lee Bennett Hopkins. Reprinted by permission of Curtis Brown, Ltd. Copyright © 1974 by Lee Bennett Hopkins.

E. P. Dutton, Inc. for "Puppy and I" from WHEN WE WERE VERY YOUNG by A. A. Milne. Copyright 1924 by E. P. Dutton, renewed 1952 by A. A. Milne. Reprinted by permission of the publisher, E. P. Dutton, a division of New American Library and McClelland and Stewart Ltd., Toronto.

Harper & Row, Publishers, Inc. for text of pp. 7–11 from ANIMAL DOCTORS: WHAT DO THEY DO? by Carla Greene. Copyright © 1967 by Carla Greene. "Cynthia in the Snow" from BRONZEVILLE BOYS AND GIRLS by Gwendolyn Brooks. Copyright © 1956 by Gwendolyn Brooks Blakely. "First Snow" from A POCKETFUL OF POEMS by Marie Louise Allen. Copyright, 1939, by Harper & Row, Publishers, Inc. Text of "The Letter" from FROG AND TOAD ARE FRIENDS by Arnold Lobel. Copyright © 1970 by Arnold Lobel. "Sam and Jane Go Camping" from THERE IS A CARROT IN MY EAR AND OTHER NOODLE TALES by Alvin Schwartz. Text copyright © 1982 by Alvin Schwartz. Reprinted by permission of Harper & Row, Publishers, Inc.

Houghton Mifflin Company for CURIOUS GEORGE RIDES A BIKE by H. A. Rey. Copyright © 1952 by H. A. Rey. Copyright renewed 1980 by Margaret Rey. Reprinted by permission of Houghton Mifflin Company. Curious George ® is a registered trademark of Margaret Rey.

Bobbi Katz for "Things to Do If You Are a Subway." Copyright © 1970 by Bobbi Katz.

Random House, Inc. for "The Fox and the Goat" and "The Lion and the Mouse" from AESOP'S FABLES by Aesop, retold by Anne Terry White. Copyright © 1964 by Anne Terry White. Reprinted by permission of Random House, Inc. "The Travels of Babar" from BABAR'S ANNIVERSARY ALBUM, by Jean and Laurent DeBrunhoff. Copyright © 1981 by Random House, Inc. Reprinted by permission of the publisher.

Beatrice Schenk de Regniers for "Keep a Poem in Your Pocket" © 1958 by Beatrice Schenk de Regniers from the book, SOMETHING SPECIAL © 1958 by Beatrice Schenk de Regniers. Reprinted by permission of the author.

Viking Penguin, Inc. for UMBRELLA by Taro Yashima. Copyright © 1958 by Taro Yashima. Reprinted by permission of Viking Penguin, Inc.

Every effort has been made to trace the ownership of all copyrighted materials in this book and to obtain permission for their use.

TABLE OF CONTENTS

TO THE STUDENT

We are born into a world that we know nothing about. As we grow, we begin to learn about the world of ideas and people. But how do we know about the worlds of the past and the dreams of the future? Reading is the answer. Reading opens the door to new worlds.

As you read this book many authors will begin to share their worlds with you. Not only what they say, but how they say it, is important. You will learn about new ideas . . . new thoughts. The beauty of all this is that all you have to do is read. Between the pages of a book you will find the real and the make-believe. You will find laughter and sadness. All of this is yours by reading.

In the Fog

Lilian Moore

Stand still.
The fog wraps you up
and no one can find you.

Walk.
The fog opens up
to let you through
and closes behind you.

Laugh and the world laughs with you.

Things to Do If You Are a Subway

Bobbi Katz

Pretend you are a dragon.
Live in underground caves.
Roar about underneath the city.
Swallow piles of people.
Spit them out at the next station.
Zoom through the darkness.
Be an express.
Go fast.
Make as much noise as you please.

There Was A Little Girl

Traditional

There was a little girl who had a little curl
Right in the middle of her forehead;
When she was good she was very, very good,
But when she was bad she was horrid.

Sam and Jane
Go Camping

Retold by Alvin Schwartz

Sam and Jane were camping out. When it got dark, they made a big fire and told stories.

"This is a story about Bill, the ghost dog," said Jane.

"It is a *very* scary story."

"I hope so," said Sam.

"Once upon a time," said Jane, "there was
a big white dog named Bill.
Bill had a very mean owner.
He wouldn't feed Bill or pet him or
anything.
Then one night—"
Suddenly Jane stopped.
She heard a strange sound.
Hmmmmmmmm!
Hmmmmmmmmmmmmm!
HMMMMMMMMMMMMMMM!
It was getting louder and louder.
"Ouch!" cried Sam.
"Something bit me!"

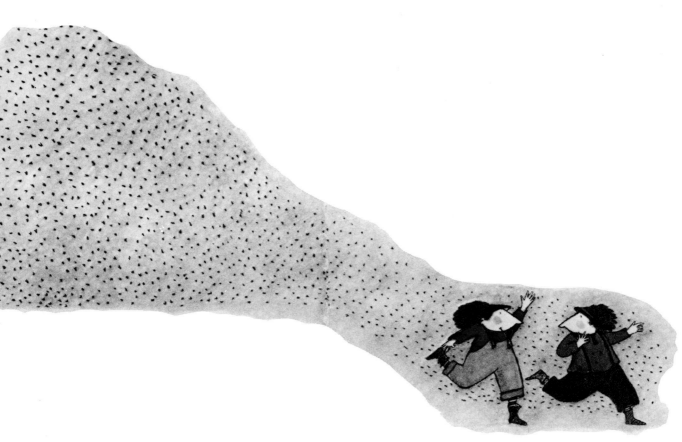

"Ouch!" yelled Jane.
"Something bit me, too!"
"It's a bunch of mosquitoes!" yelled Sam.
They jumped up and down and ran around
and waved their arms.
But the mosquitoes would not go away.
"Let's put out the fire," whispered Sam.
"They'll never find us in the dark."
They put out the fire and sat down on
a rock.

A mosquito flew by, then disappeared.
It was as quiet as a graveyard.
"They are gone!" whispered Jane.
"I think so," whispered Sam.
Then some fireflies flew by.
"Oh, no!" Sam groaned.
"They are back!
And now they are looking for us with
flashlights."

I'M GLAD THE SKY IS PAINTED BLUE

Anonymous

I'm glad the sky is painted blue,
And the earth is painted green,
With such a lot of nice fresh air
All sandwiched in between.

FUZZY WUZZY

Anonymous

Fuzzy Wuzzy was a bear;
Fuzzy Wuzzy had no hair.
So Fuzzy Wuzzy wasn't fuzzy. Was he?

If at first you don't succeed,
try, try again.

Mud Puddle
Robert N. Munsch

Jule Ann's mother bought her clean new clothes.

Jule Ann put on a clean new shirt, clean pants, and went out to play under the apple tree in the back yard.

12

Unfortunately, there was a mud puddle hiding up in the apple tree.

It saw Jule Ann and jumped right on her head.

She got completely all over muddy.

Even her ears were full of mud.

Jule Ann ran inside yelling, "Mummy, Mummy! A Mud Puddle jumped on me."

Her mother took off all Jule Ann's clothes and dropped her into a big bathtub. She scrubbed Jule Ann till she was red all over.

Jule Ann put on a clean new shirt,
clean new pants and looked carefully out
the door.

There was no mud puddle anywhere,
so Jule Ann went to play in the sand box
next to the house.

Unfortunately, there was a mud puddle
hiding on the roof.

14

It jumped right on Jule Ann's head and
she got completely all over muddy. Even
her mouth was full of mud.

Jule Ann ran inside yelling, "Mummy,
Mummy! A Mud Puddle jumped on me."

15

Jule Ann's mother took off all Jule
Ann's clothes and dropped Jule Ann into a
big bathtub full of water. She scrubbed Jule
Ann till she was red all over.

Jule Ann put on a clean new shirt,
clean new pants and then she put on a big
yellow raincoat with a hood. She marched
out to the middle of the yard and yelled,
"Hey, Mud Puddle!"

Nothing happened. Jule Ann started to
get hot, so she slowly pulled back her hood.

Nothing happened, so she slowly took
off her raincoat.

As soon as her coat was off the mud puddle ran from behind the dog house and jumped right on Jule Ann's head. She got completely all over muddy. Even her nose was full of mud.

Jule Ann ran inside yelling, "Mummy, Mummy! A Mud Puddle jumped on me."

Jule Ann's mother took off all Jule Ann's clothes and dropped her into a big bathtub full of water. She scrubbed Jule Ann till she was red all over.

Jule Ann put on a clean new shirt, new pants and then she sat beside the door, for she was afraid to go outside.

Suddenly she had an idea!

She got two huge bars of smelly orange soap and hid them in her pockets.

Then she ran to the middle of the yard and yelled, "Hey, Mud Puddle!"

The mud puddle jumped over the fence and ran right toward her.

Jule Ann threw a bar of soap right into the mud puddle's middle.

The mud puddle stopped.

Jule Ann threw the other bar of soap into the mud puddle.

The mud puddle said, "Awk, Yuck, Wackh!" It jumped over the fence and never came back.

Old Mother Hubbard

Traditional

Old Mother Hubbard
Went to the cupboard,
To fetch her poor dog a bone;

When she got there
The cupboard was bare,
And so the poor dog had none.

She went to the baker's
To buy him some bread,
But when she came back
The poor dog was dead.

She went to the joiner's
To buy him a coffin,
But when she came back
The poor dog was laughing.

She went to the barber's
To buy him a wig,
But when she came back
He was dancing a jig.

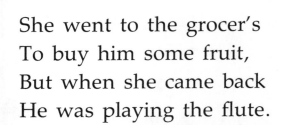

She went to the grocer's
To buy him some fruit,
But when she came back
He was playing the flute.

She went to the seamstress
To buy him some linen,
But when she came back
The dog was a-spinning.

She went to the cobbler's
To buy him some shoes,
But when she came back
He was reading the news.

She went to the fishmonger's
To buy him some fish,
But when she came back
He was licking the dish.

She went to the tailor's
To buy him a coat,
But when she came back
He was riding a goat.

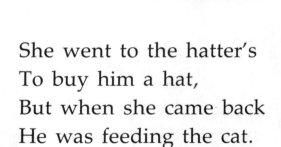

She went to the hatter's
To buy him a hat,
But when she came back
He was feeding the cat.

She took a clean dish
To get him some tripe,
But when she came back
He was smoking a pipe.

She went to the hosier's
To buy him some hose,
But when she came back
He was dressed in his clothes.

The dame made a curtsy,
The dog made a bow;
The dame said, Your servant,
The dog said, Bow-wow.

First Snow

Marie Louise Allen

Snow makes whiteness where it falls.
The bushes look like popcorn-balls.
And places where I always play,
Look like somewhere else today.

Cynthia in the Snow
Gwendolyn Brooks

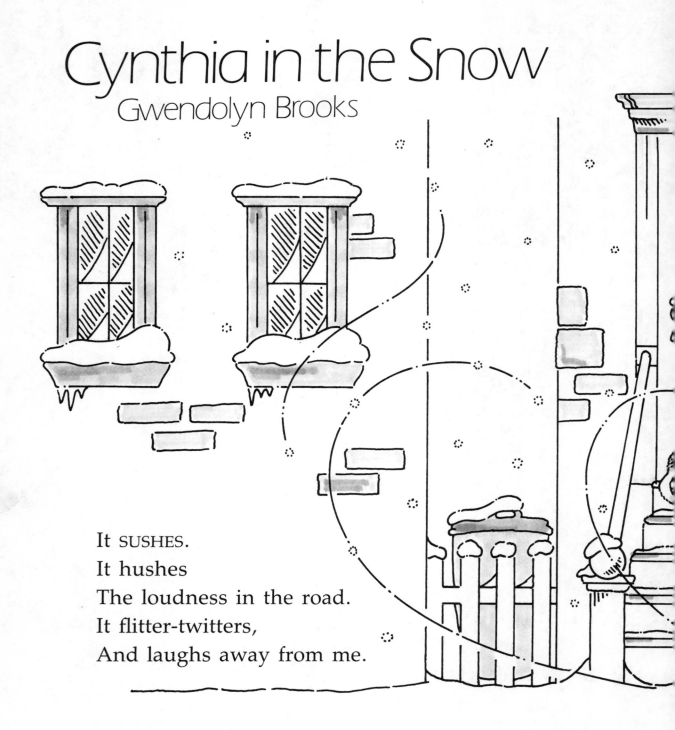

It SUSHES.
It hushes
The loudness in the road.
It flitter-twitters,
And laughs away from me.

It laughs a lovely whiteness,
And whitely whirs away,
To be
Some otherwhere,
Still white as milk or shirts.
So beautiful it hurts.

HUSH LITTLE BABY
Traditional

Hush little baby,
don't say a word,
Daddy's gonna buy you
a mockingbird.
And if that mockingbird
won't sing,
Daddy's gonna buy you
a diamond ring.

And if that diamond ring
is brass,
Daddy's gonna buy you
a looking glass.

And if that looking glass
gets broke,
Daddy's gonna buy you
a billy goat.

And if that billy goat
won't pull,
Daddy's gonna buy you
a cart and bull.

30

And if that cart and bull
turn over,
Daddy's gonna buy you
a dog named Rover.

And if that dog named Rover
    won't bark,
Daddy's gonna buy you
    a horse and cart.

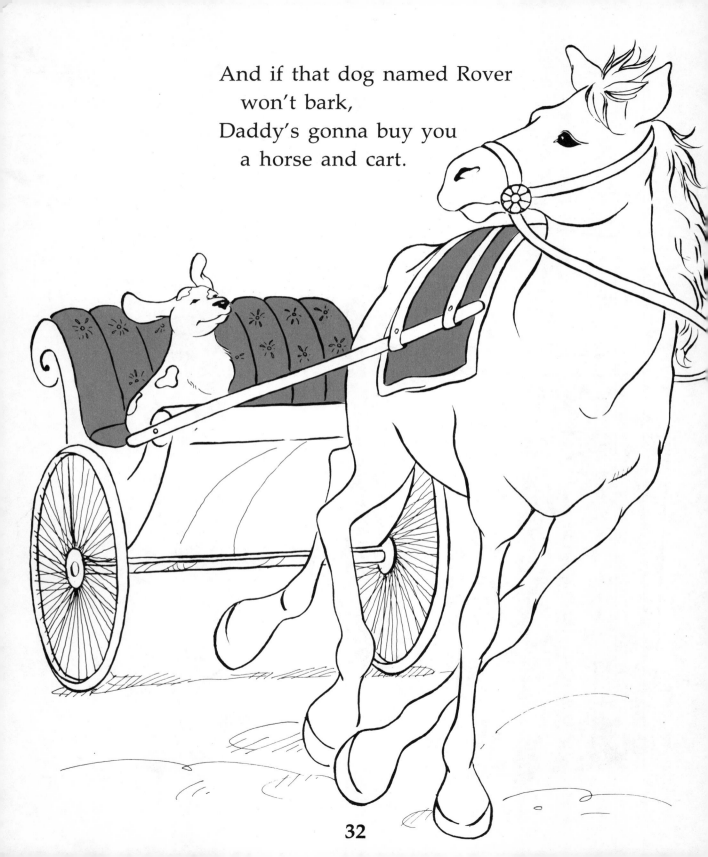

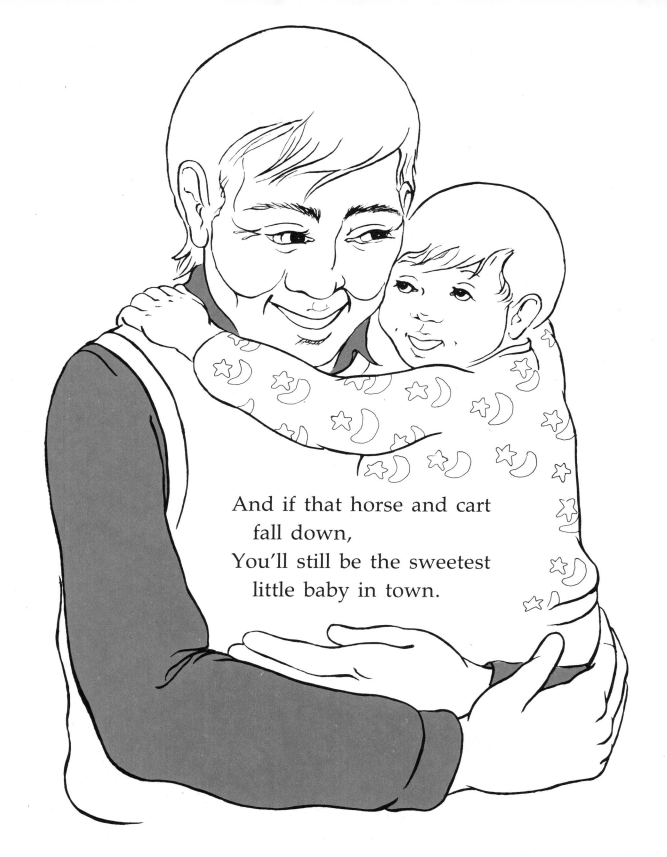

And if that horse and cart
fall down,
You'll still be the sweetest
little baby in town.

NIGHTTIME

Lee Bennett Hopkins

How do dreams know
    just when to creep

Into my head
    when I fall off to sleep?

UMBRELLA

Taro Yashima

 *Haru* (Spring)

Momo is the name of a little girl
who was born in New York.
The word *Momo* means "the peach" in Japan
where her father and mother used to live.

On her third birthday
Momo was given two presents—
red rubber boots and an umbrella!
They pleased her so much
that she even woke up that midnight
to take another look at them.

 *Natsu* (Summer)

Unfortunately
it was still Indian summer,
and the sun was bright.

Every morning
Momo asked her mother,
who used to take her
to the nearby nursery school,
"Why the rain doesn't fall?"
The answer was always the same:
"Wait, wait; it will come."

One morning
Momo was more impatient than ever,
because the sun
was brighter than ever.
But, strangely enough,
a splendid idea made her jump up
when she was watching
the sunshine in her milk glass.
"I need my umbrella.
The sunshine bothers my eyes!"
But her mother said,
"You know you can enjoy the sunshine
better without the umbrella.
Let's keep it for a rainy day."

Next morning
Momo was still unhappy,
because she still
could not use her umbrella.

But, strangely enough,
another idea made her jump up
when she was watching
the people on the street.
"I certainly need my umbrella today!
The wind must bother my eyes!"
But her mother said,
"The wind might blow your umbrella away.
Let's keep it for a rainy day."

 *Ame* (Rain)

It was many, many days later
that finally the rain fell.
Momo was wakened
by her mother's voice—
"Get up! Get up! What a surprise for you!"

Momo did not stop to wash her face.
She even pulled the boots
onto her bare feet—
she was so excited.

The pavement was all wet and new—
doodling she had drawn yesterday
was not there any more.
Instead, raindrops
were jumping all over,
like the tiny people dancing.

The street was crowded and noisy,
but she whispered to herself,
"I must walk straight,
like a grown-up-lady!"

On the umbrella,
raindrops made a wonderful music
she never had heard before—

> *Bon polo*
> *bon polo*
> *ponpolo ponpolo*
> *ponpolo ponpolo*
> *bolo bolo ponpolo*
> *bolo bolo ponpolo*
> *boto boto ponpolo*
> *boto boto ponpolo*

43

The rain did not stop all day long.
Momo watched it at times while she was
playing the games at the nursery school.

She did not forget her umbrella
when her father came
to take her home.
She used to forget
her mittens or her scarf so easily—
but not her umbrella.

The street was crowded and noisy,
but she whispered to herself,
"I must walk straight,
like a grown-up-lady!"

On her umbrella, the raindrops
make the wonderful music—

> *Bon polo*
> *bon polo*
> *ponpolo ponpolo*
> *ponpolo ponpolo*
> *bolo bolo ponpolo*
> *bolo bolo ponpolo*
> *boto boto ponpolo*
> *boto boto ponpolo*

all the way home.

桃 *Momo* (Peach)

Momo is a big girl now,
and this is a story
she does not remember at all.

Does she remember or not,
it was not only the first day in her life
that she used her umbrella,
it was also the first day in her life
that she walked alone,
without holding either
her mother's or her father's hand.

Hitch your wagon to a star.

TWINKLE, TWINKLE
Traditional

Twinkle, twinkle, little star,
How I wonder what you are!
Up above the world so high,
Like a diamond in the sky.

When the blazing sun is gone,
When he nothing shines upon,
Then you show your little light,
Twinkle, twinkle, all the night.

Mary Ann the Witch Girl

Pamela Espeland and Marilyn Waniek

Mary Ann the witch girl
Sneaks out at night
Closes the screen door
Locks it up tight
Faces the apple tree
Turns toward the house
Whispers a magic spell
Squeaks like a mouse
Chooses a special star
Then makes two wishes . . .

And passes arithmetic
and NEVER does dishes!

Keep
a
Poem
in
Your Pocket

Beatrice Schenk de Regniers

Keep a poem in your pocket
and a picture in your head
and you'll never feel lonely
at night when you're in bed.

The little poem will sing to you
the little picture bring to you
a dozen dreams to dance to you
at night when you're in bed.

So—
Keep a picture in your pocket
and a poem in your head
and you'll never feel lonely
at night when you're in bed.

53

The Travels of
BABAR

Jean de Brunhoff

Babar, the young King of the elephants, and
his wife, Queen Celeste, were going on
their wedding trip in a balloon. "Good-bye!
See you soon!" cried the elephants as they
watched the balloon rise and drift away.

Arthur, Babar's little cousin, waved his
beret. Old Cornelius, who was chief over all

the elephants when the King was away, anxiously sighed, "I do hope they won't have any accidents!"

The country of the elephants was now far away. The balloon glided noiselessly in the sky. Babar and Celeste admired the landscape below. What a beautiful journey! The air was balmy, the wind was gentle. There was the ocean, the big blue ocean.

Suddenly the balloon was blown out to sea by a violent storm. Babar and Celeste trembled with fear and clung to the basket.

By extraordinary good fortune, just as the balloon was about to fall into the sea, a final puff of wind blew it to an island, where it flattened out and collapsed.

"You aren't hurt, Celeste, are you?" Babar inquired anxiously. "No! Well then, look, we are saved!"

Leaving the wrecked balloon on the beach, Babar and Celeste picked up their belongings and went off to seek shelter.

Celeste hung up their clothes to dry while Babar lighted a fire and began preparing breakfast.

Babar and Celeste settled themselves
comfortably. They set up their tent. Then
they sat on some large stones and ate an
excellent rice broth well-sweetened and
cooked to perfection. "We are not so badly
off," said Babar.

After breakfast Babar and Celeste rested
on the seashore. Suddenly a whale came to
the surface and spouted. Babar said, "Good
morning, Mrs. Whale. I am Babar and here
is my wife, Celeste. We have had a balloon
accident. Can you help us to get away from
here?"

"I will be very happy to help you," said
the whale. "Quick, get on my back and
hold tight so you don't slip off. Are you
ready? Get set. Let's go!"

A few days later Babar and Celeste were resting on a reef. Just then a school of little fish swam by.

"I am going to eat up some of these," said the whale. "I'll be back in a minute." But she did not come back. She forgot!

After hours spent on their little reef, without even a drop of fresh water, they finally spied a ship passing quite near them. It was a big steamer with three funnels.

Babar and Celeste called out and yelled as loudly as they could, but no one heard them. They tried signaling with their trunks and with their arms. Would they ever attract someone's attention?

Finally somebody saw them! A lifeboat
rescued Babar and Celeste while the excited
passengers all watched.

A week later the huge ship steamed
slowly into a big harbor. All the passengers
went down the gangplank. Babar and
Celeste were not allowed to go. They had
lost their crowns, so no one believed they
were King and Queen of the elephants.

The Captain of the ship ordered them
locked up in the ship's stables. "They give
us straw to sleep on!" cried Babar angrily.

The Captain came in with an animal trainer, Fernando. "You can have these elephants for your circus," he said. Fernando led away his two pupils.

"Be patient, Babar," whispered Celeste. "We will get home somehow and see Cornelius and Arthur."

Fernando took Babar and Celeste to his circus.

He made Babar play a trumpet while

Celeste danced! They were very unhappy.

One day the circus came to the town where Babar had met his friend the Old Lady. So, at night, while Fernando was in bed, Babar and Celeste escaped and went to find her. He had never forgotten her.

Babar found the house easily and rang the bell. The Old Lady put on her wrapper, stepped out onto her balcony, and called, "Who's there?"

"Babar and Celeste," they answered her.

The Old Lady was overjoyed. Babar and Celeste were happy too, for they would never have to go back to the circus. Soon they would rejoin Arthur and Cornelius. The Old Lady promised to help them.

At the circus their escape was soon discovered.

"Stop! Thief! My elephants have been stolen!" cried the excited Fernando.

"Little ones, oh little ones, where are
you hiding?" the clowns called.

But Babar and Celeste would not be
caught again. They were on their way to the

station with the Old Lady. They needed a few days' rest before returning to their own land.

The three of them went to the mountains to enjoy the fresh air and try a little skiing.

Then they left by plane to return home.
Babar was anxious to show the Old Lady
his beautiful country. But when they got
there, nothing was left of the great forest.
There were no flowers, no birds. Everyone
was sad.

"Alas," said Cornelius. "The
rhinoceroses have declared war on us."
Celeste and the Old Lady took care of the

wounded elephants and Babar went off to
join the elephant army.

At the camp of the rhinoceroses the
soldiers were awaiting orders. "We will once
again defeat the elephants," they thought.
"Then the war will be over and we can all
go home."

Spiteful old Rataxes maliciously said to
his friend, General Pamir: "Hah! Hah! Hah!
Pretty soon we will tweak the ears of this
young King Babar and punish that rascal
Arthur."

At the camp of the elephants Babar
brought his army new courage. He
disguised his biggest soldiers, painting their
tails bright red, and near their tails on either
side he painted large, frightening eyes.

Arthur set to work making wigs. He
worked as hard as he could so he would be
forgiven. The war was really Arthur's fault.
It had started when that rascal Arthur had
tied a big firecracker to Rataxes's tail.

On the day of the battle, at just the right moment, the disguised elephants came out of hiding. Babar's bright idea succeeded!

The rhinoceroses thought they were monsters and, terrified, they retreated in great disorder. King Babar was a mighty fine general.

The rhinoceroses fled and kept running! Pamir and Rataxes were taken prisoner and hung their heads in shame. What a glorious day for the elephants! In chorus they all cried:

"Bravo, Babar, bravo! Victory! Victory! The war is over! How perfectly splendid!"

The next day, before all of the elephants, Babar and Celeste put on their royal garments and their new crowns and rewarded the Old Lady, who had been so good to them and had cared for the wounded. They gave her eleven singing canaries and a cunning little monkey.

After the ceremony Babar, Celeste, and
the Old Lady sat and chatted under the
palm trees. "And what are we going to do
next?" asked the Old Lady.

"I am going to try to rule my kingdom
wisely," answered Babar, "and if you will
remain with us, you can help me make my
subjects happy."

A friend in need
is a friend indeed.

The Lion and the Mouse

Aesop

Retold by Anne Terry White

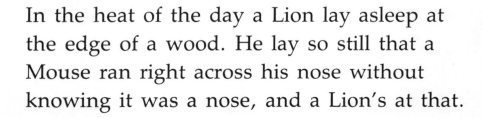

In the heat of the day a Lion lay asleep at
the edge of a wood. He lay so still that a
Mouse ran right across his nose without
knowing it was a nose, and a Lion's at that.

Bang! The Lion clapped his paw to his face and felt something caught. It was furry. Lazily he opened his eyes. He lifted up one side of his huge paw just a little bit to see what was under it and was amused to find a Mouse.

"Spare me, Great King!" he heard the little creature squeak in its tiny voice. "I didn't mean to do it! Let me go, and someday I will repay you."

"That's very funny," said the Lion, and he laughed. "How can a little thing like you help me, the great King of Beasts?"

"I don't know," the Mouse replied, "but a little creature *can* sometimes help a big one."

"Well, you have made me laugh," the Lion said, "which is something I seldom do. And anyway, you would hardly make half a mouthful. So——" He raised his paw and let the Mouse go.

A few days later the Lion was caught in a hunter's net. The woods rang with his angry roaring and the little Mouse heard him.

"That is my kind Lion!" she cried. "He is in trouble!" As fast as she could, she ran toward the spot from which the roaring came, and there he was. The Lion was thrashing around so in the net that the Mouse didn't dare to come near for fear of being crushed.

"O King, be patient!" she cried. "I will gnaw through the ropes and set you free."

So the Lion lay still while the Mouse worked away with her sharp teeth. And in a short time he was able to creep out of the net.

"You see? I told you I would repay you," the Mouse said happily. "A little creature sometimes really can help a big one."

And the Lion had to admit it was true.

Little friends may prove to be great friends.

Curious George rides a bike

H. A. Rey

This is George.

He lived with his friend, the man with the yellow hat. He was a good little monkey and always very curious.

This morning George was curious the moment he woke up because he knew it was a special day . . .

At breakfast George's friend said:
"Today we are going to celebrate because
just three years ago this day I brought you
home with me from the jungle. So tonight
I'll take you to the animal show. But first I
have a surprise for you."

He took George out to the yard where a
big box was standing. George was very
curious.

Out of the box came a bicycle. George
was delighted; that's what he had always
wanted. He knew how to ride a bicycle but
he had never had one of his own.

"I must go now," said the man, "but
I'll be back in time for the show. Be careful
with your new bike and keep close to the
house while I am gone!"

George could ride very well. He could
even do all sorts of tricks (monkeys are
good at that).

For instance he could ride this way,
with both hands off the handle bar,

and he could ride this way, like a cowboy
on a wild bronco, and he could also ride
backwards.

But after a while George got tired of doing
tricks and went out into the street.

The newsboy was just passing by with his
bag full of papers. "It's a fine bike you have
there," he said to George. "How would you
like to help me deliver the papers?"

He handed George the bag and told
him to do one side of the street first and
then turn back and do the other side.

George was very proud as he rode off
with his bag.

He started to deliver the papers on one side of the street as he had been told. When he came to the last house he saw a little river in the distance. George was curious: he wanted to know what the river was like, so instead of turning back to deliver the rest of the papers he just went on.

There was a lot to see at the river: a
man was fishing from the bridge, a duck
family was paddling downstream, and two
boys were playing with their boats. George
would have liked to stop and look at the
boats, but he was afraid the boys might find
out that he had not delivered all the papers.
So he rode on.

While riding along George kept thinking
of boats all the time. It would be such fun
to have a boat—but how could he get one?
He thought and thought—and then he had
an idea.

He got off the bicycle, took a
newspaper out of the bag and began to
fold it.

First he folded down the corners,
like this,

95

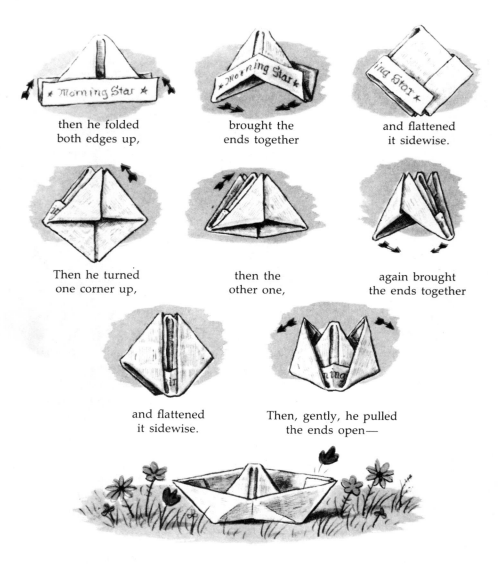

then he folded
both edges up,

brought the
ends together

and flattened
it sidewise.

Then he turned
one corner up,

then the
other one,

again brought
the ends together

and flattened
it sidewise.

Then, gently, he pulled
the ends open—

and there was his BOAT!

Now the moment had come to launch the boat. Would it float? It did!

So George decided to make some more boats. Finally he had used up all the papers and had made so many boats that he could not count them—a whole fleet.

Watching his fleet sailing down the
river George felt like an admiral. But
watching his fleet he forgot to watch where
he was going—

suddenly there was a terrible jolt: the
bicycle had hit a rock and George flew off
the seat, head first.

Luckily George was not hurt, but the
front wheel of the bicycle was all out of
shape and the tire was blown out.

George tried to ride the bicycle, but of course it wouldn't go. So he started carrying it, but it soon got too heavy.

George did not know WHAT to do: his
new bike was spoiled, the newspapers were
gone. He wished he had listened to his
friend and kept close to the house. Now he
just stood there and cried . . .

Suddenly his face brightened. Why—he
had forgotten that he could ride on one
wheel! He tried it and it worked.

He had hardly started out again when
he saw something he had never seen before:
rolling toward him came an enormous
tractor with huge trailers behind it. Looking

out of the trailers were all sorts of animals.
To George it looked like a Zoo on wheels.
The tractor stopped and two men jumped out.

"Well, well," said one of the men, "a little monkey who can ride a bike bronco fashion! We can use you in our animal show tonight. I am the director of the show and this is Bob. He can straighten your wheel

and fix that flat in no time and then we'll take you along to the place where the show is going to be."

So the three of them got into the cab
and drove off. "Maybe you could play a
fanfare while you ride your bike in the
show," the director said. "I have a bugle for
you right here, and later on you'll get a
green coat and a cap just like Bob's."

On the show grounds everybody was
busy getting things ready for the show. "I
must do some work now," said the director.
"Meanwhile you may have a look around

and get acquainted with all the animals—
but you must not feed them, especially the
ostrich because he will eat anything and
might get very sick afterwards."

George was curious: would the ostrich
really eat anything? He wouldn't eat a
bugle—or would he? George went a little
closer to the cage—and before he knew it

the ostrich had snatched the bugle and tried
to swallow it. But a bugle is hard to
swallow, even for an ostrich; it got stuck in
his throat. Funny sounds came out of the
bugle as the ostrich was struggling with it,
all blue in the face.

George was frightened.

Fortunately the men had heard the
noise. They came rushing to the cage and
got the bugle out of the ostrich's throat just
in time.

The director was very angry with George. "We cannot use little monkeys who don't do as they are told," he said. "Of course you cannot take part in the show now. We will have to send you home."

George had to sit on a bench all by himself and nobody even looked at him. He was terribly sorry for what he had done but now it was too late. He had spoiled everything.

   Meanwhile the ostrich, always hungry,
had got hold of a string dangling near his
cage. This happened to be the string which
held the door to the cage of the baby bear.
As the ostrich nibbled at it the door
opened—and the baby bear got out.

He ran away as fast as he could and made straight for a high tree near the camp.

Nobody had seen it but George—and George was not supposed to leave his bench. But this was an emergency, so he jumped up, grabbed the bugle, and blew as loud as he could. Then he rushed to his bicycle.

The men had heard the alarm and thought at first that George had been naughty again. But when they saw the empty cage and the ostrich nibbling at the string, they knew what had happened.

George raced toward the tree, far ahead of the men.

By now the bear had climbed quite high—and this was dangerous because little bears can climb up a tree easily but coming down is much harder; they may fall and get hurt.

The men were worried. They did not know how to get him down safely.

But George had his plan: with the bag
over his shoulder he went up the tree as
fast as only a monkey can,

and when he reached the baby bear he put
him in his bag and carefully let him down
so that the men could safely catch him.

Everybody cheered when George had come down from the tree. "You are a brave little monkey," said the director, "you saved the baby bear's life. Now you'll get your coat back and of course you may ride your bike and play the bugle in the show."

Finally the show
was on. The whole
town had come to
see it, and how

surprised they were
to discover George
on his bike right in
the middle of it!

The newsboy was there, too, and also the man with the yellow hat who had been looking for George everywhere and was happy to have found him at last.
The newsboy was glad to have his bag again, and the people from the other side of the street whose papers George had made into boats were not angry with him any more.

George!

When the time had come for George to say goodbye, the director let him keep the coat and the cap and the bugle. And then George and his friend got into the car and went . . .

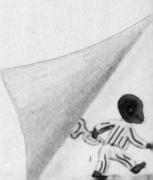

good Night!

ANIMAL DOCTORS
WHAT DO THEY DO?

Carla Greene

Do you have a pet?
A dog or a cat? A hamster?
A snake or a lizard?

A canary or a parakeet?
If you have any kind of pet, you may know
an animal doctor.

It takes a long time to become an animal doctor.
An animal doctor goes to college for at least six years.

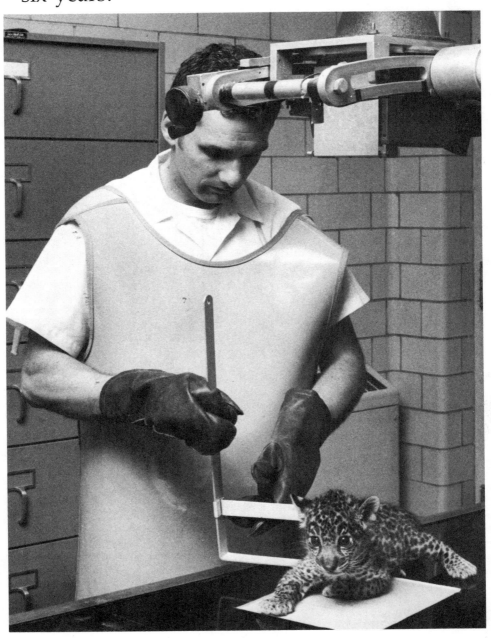

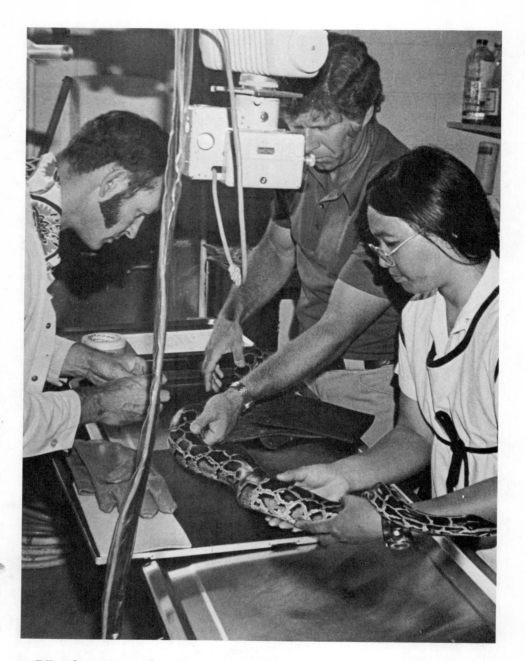

He learns about many kinds of animals,
reptiles, and birds.
He learns about animal foods and
medicines.

He looks into a microscope and sees the
germs that make animals sick.
He learns to take X rays to see if an animal
has broken bones.
He learns to set broken bones so they
will mend.

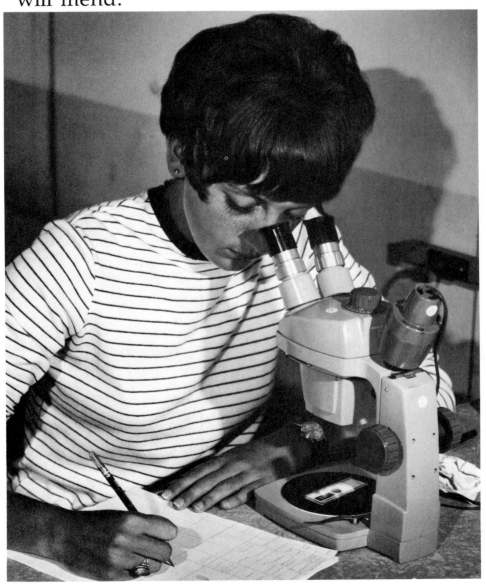

Some animal doctors live in the city.
They take care of city pets.
Some animal doctors live in the country.
They take care of farm animals and
country pets.

Some animal doctors take care of wild
animals in a zoo or circus.
A few animal doctors look after animals that
are sent into outer space.

Puppy and I

A. A. Milne

I met a man as I went walking;
We got talking,
Man and I.
"Where are you going to, Man?" I said
(I said to the Man as he went by).
"Down to the village, to get some bread.
Will you come with me?" "No, not I."

I met a Horse as I went walking;
We got talking,
Horse and I.
"Where are you going to, Horse, today?"
(I said to the Horse as he went by).
"Down to the village to get some hay.
Will you come with me?" "No, not I."

I met a Woman as I went walking;
We got talking,
Woman and I.

"Where are you going to, Woman, so early?"
(I said to the Woman as she went by).
"Down to the village to get some barley.
Will you come with me?" "No, not I."

I met some Rabbits as I went walking;
We got talking,
Rabbits and I.
"Where are you going in your brown fur
    coats?"
(I said to the Rabbits as they went by).
"Down to the village to get some oats.
Will you come with us?" "No, not I."

I met a Puppy as I went walking;
We got talking,
Puppy and I.
"Where are you going this nice fine day?"
(I said to the Puppy as he went by).
"Up in the hills to roll and play."
"*I'll* come with you, Puppy," said I.

The Fox and the Goat

Aesop

Retold by Anne Terry White

One day a Fox was nosing around a well.
By bad luck his foot slipped on a wet stone
and he fell in. The water wasn't deep, but
the well was. And though he wore himself
out trying to get out, the Fox could not
do it.

"What in the world are you doing down there in the well?" he heard someone ask. He looked up. There stood a Goat peering down in the well.

The Fox's spirits rose. He saw hope ahead.

"Enjoying myself!" he replied. "They say there will be no rain for a long time and all the wells will go dry. So I am drinking my fill before it happens. Come on down— the water's fine."

The foolish Goat didn't stop to think.
He jumped right in.

The Fox, of course, wanted to use him for a ladder and leaped at once on the Goat's back. Then he set one foot on his horns and jumped out of the well.

"Good-by, my friend," he called out from above. "And next time, silly Goat, look before you leap!"

Think how you will get out before you get in.

The Letter

Arnold Lobel

Toad was sitting on his front porch.
Frog came along and said,
"What is the matter, Toad?
You are looking sad."
"Yes," said Toad.
"This is my sad time of day.

It is the time
when I wait for the mail to come.
It always makes me very unhappy."
"Why is that?" asked Frog.
"Because I never get any mail,"
said Toad.
"Not ever?" asked Frog.
"No, never," said Toad.
"No one has ever sent me a letter.
Every day my mailbox is empty.
That is why waiting for the mail
is a sad time for me."
Frog and Toad sat on the porch,
feeling sad together.

Then Frog said,
"I have to go home now, Toad.
There is something that I must do."
Frog hurried home.
He found a pencil
and a piece of paper.
He wrote on the paper.
He put the paper in an envelope.
On the envelope he wrote
"A LETTER FOR TOAD."
Frog ran out of his house.
He saw a snail that he knew.
"Snail," said Frog, "please take
this letter to Toad's house
and put it in his mailbox."

"Sure," said the snail. "Right away."
Then Frog ran back to Toad's house.
Toad was in bed, taking a nap.
"Toad," said Frog,
"I think you should get up
and wait for the mail some more."
"No," said Toad,
"I am tired of waiting for the mail."
Frog looked out of the window
at Toad's mailbox.

The snail was not there yet.
"Toad," said Frog, "you never know
when someone may send you a letter."
"No, no," said Toad. "I do not think
anyone will ever send me a letter."
Frog looked out of the window.
The snail was not there yet.
"But, Toad," said Frog,
"someone may send you a letter today."
"Don't be silly," said Toad.
"No one has ever sent me
a letter before, and no one
will send me a letter today."
Frog looked out of the window.
The snail was still not there.

"Frog, why do you keep looking
out of the window?" asked Toad.
"Because now I am waiting
for the mail," said Frog.
"But there will not be any," said Toad.
"Oh, yes there will," said Frog,
"because I have sent you a letter."
"You have?" said Toad.
"What did you write in the letter?"

Frog said, "I wrote
'Dear Toad, I am glad
that you are my best friend.
Your best friend, Frog.' "
"Oh," said Toad,
"that makes a very good letter."
Then Frog and Toad went out
onto the front porch
to wait for the mail.

They sat there,
feeling happy together.
Frog and Toad waited a long time.
Four days later
the snail got to Toad's house
and gave him the letter from Frog.
Toad was very pleased to have it.